The New Room

by Anne Giulieri
illustrated by Samantha Chaffey

"Is this where we are going to live?" asked Nick.

"Yes," said Dad.
"Let's take a look inside."

3

"This is your new room, boys,"
said Dad.

"Oh, dear," said Nick.
"The beds we had
at the old house
will not fit in here!"

"Then we will have to get beds that **will** fit!" said Dad.
"Let's take a look in the truck."

"Oh, look!" shouted Nick.
"I can see two beds
in the truck."

"Yes," said Tom.
"And I can see a slide
and a ladder, too."

"Yes," laughed Dad.
"They are for your
new bunk beds."

"The beds can go up first,"
said Dad.
"Then the ladder and the slide
can go up next."

"The bunk beds will be good
to sleep in," said Tom.
"They will be fun, too!"

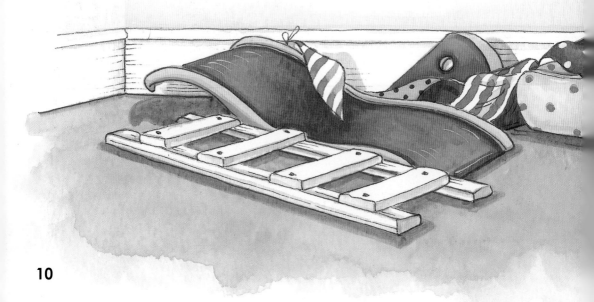

11

"Look at me," said Tom.

"I'm under your bed."

"Look at me," said Nick.

"I'm going up the ladder."

"Tom!" laughed Nick.
"Look at me.
I'm over your bed."

"Look at me," laughed Tom.
"I'm going down the slide."

"Thank you, Dad,"
said Nick and Tom.
"We love the new beds.
And we love the new house, too!"

a Capstone company — publishers for children

Engage Literacy is published in the UK by Raintree.
Raintree is an imprint of Capstone Global Library Limited, a company
incorporated in England and Wales having its registered office at 264
Banbury Road, Oxford, OX2 7DY – Registered company number:
6695582

www.raintree.co.uk

The New Room
ISBN: 978-1-4747-7235-8

Text copyright © Anne Giulieri 2015

10 9 8 7 6 5 4 3 2
Printed and bound in India

Early
Level 11
Fiction

Nick and Tom have a new
house and a new room.
Will the beds
fit into the new room?

raintree
a Capstone company—publishers for children
www.raintree.co.uk

ISBN 978-1-4747-7235-8

9 781474 772358

SOUNDS-WRITE
First Rate Phonics

The can man

Main Collection
Initial Code Unit 3

Written by Kate Burlison
Illustrated by Celia Arcos

Sam and Bob got a bag of cans.
In the bag is a big can.

Sam pops it on the mat. Bob put
a can on top of the big can.

'Put the cans in the bin!' said Mum.
But Sam and Bob did not.

Sam got a hat. Bob got a mac.

Bob put the mac on the cans.
'The hat can sit on top,' said Sam.

'It is a man,' said Bob.
'A can man,' said Sam.

Sam got a can. Sam hit the hat. Bam!
Bob got a can.
Bob hit the man. Bam!

'It is a man!' said Mum.

'A can man!' said Bob and Sam.